the fish who
searched for water

to all who seek

D1158179

© 2016 Conscious Stories LLC

Illustrations by Marcel Marais

Published by
Conscious Stories LLC
4800 Baseline Rd,
Suite E104-365
Boulder, CO
80303
USA

www.consciousstories.com

First Edition
Library of Congress
Control Number: 2017901956
ISBN 978-1-943750-06-1

The last 20 minutes of every day are precious.

Dear parents, teachers, and readers,

This story has been gift-wrapped with two simple mindfulness practices to help you connect more deeply with your children in the last 20 minutes of each day.

● Quietly set your intention for calm, open connection.

● Then start your story time with the **Snuggle Breathing Meditation**. Read each line aloud and take slow, deep breaths together in order to relax and be present.

● At the end of the story you will find **The Love Hunt**. The questions help your children know that they are surrounded by love wherever they are, which is the moral of our story. Have fun finding love together.

Enjoy Snuggling into Togetherness!

Andrew

Snuggle Breathing

Our story begins with us breathing together.
Say each line aloud and then
take a slow deep breath in and out.

I breathe for me

I breathe for you

I breathe for us

I breathe for all that surrounds us

Once upon a time
There was a little fish

Who never felt at home.
He had a special wish.

"Where, oh where, is water?"
sought the little fish.
"I will shrivel up if I can't fulfill this wish."

Is it here?

Or here?

Maybe here?

7

No one had the answers
That he'd believe or trust,

So onward he went swimming,
Thinking that he must.

He swam...

And swam...

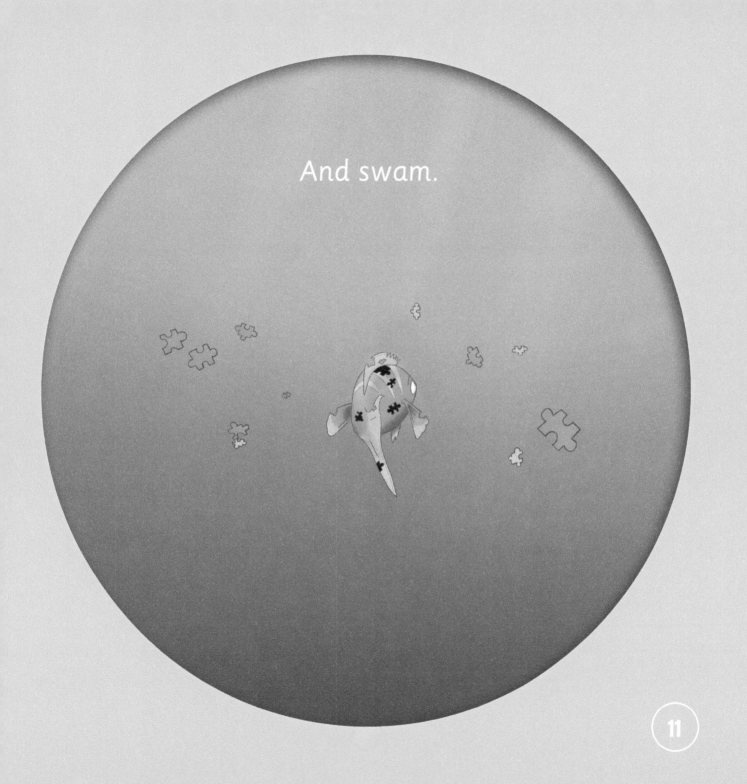

And swam.

He paused at a few places
To have a little sip,

Finding some refreshment
On his tiresome trip.

On he swam,
Thirsty for more.
What he had found
Couldn't be all.

13

One day he leapt up in the air.

It was brave and bold
And done on a dare.

He thought,
"If I can get the view of a bird

I'll soon find water,"
Or so he had heard.

15

He leapt in the air,
Took a great big gasp,

BUT his gills shut down,
Drowned with the blast.

Thankfully gravity pulled him back in
To where he could breathe
And where he could swim.

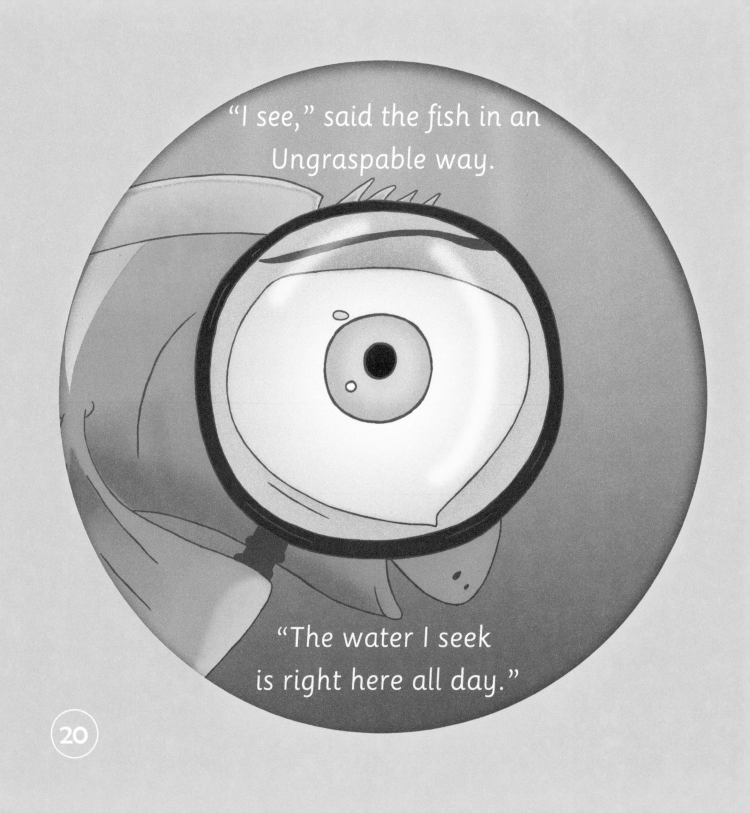

The water I seek
Surrounds me right now.
Somehow it seems it's inside me.

OH WOW!

I don't need to swim
Or to seek or to look

To discover the water
I simply mistook.

I don't need to struggle
Or quest or breathe air
To experience water.
IT'S ALREADY THERE!"

23

Where did you find love today?

We all search for love in our own way. Sometimes we find love, but don't recognize it. Sometimes, love is too close to see.

Answer the questions in **The Love Hunt** and enjoy a moment together.

24

Count your blessings

The Love Hunt

1

Where did you look for love today?

2

Who showed you love today?

3

When did you forget love today?

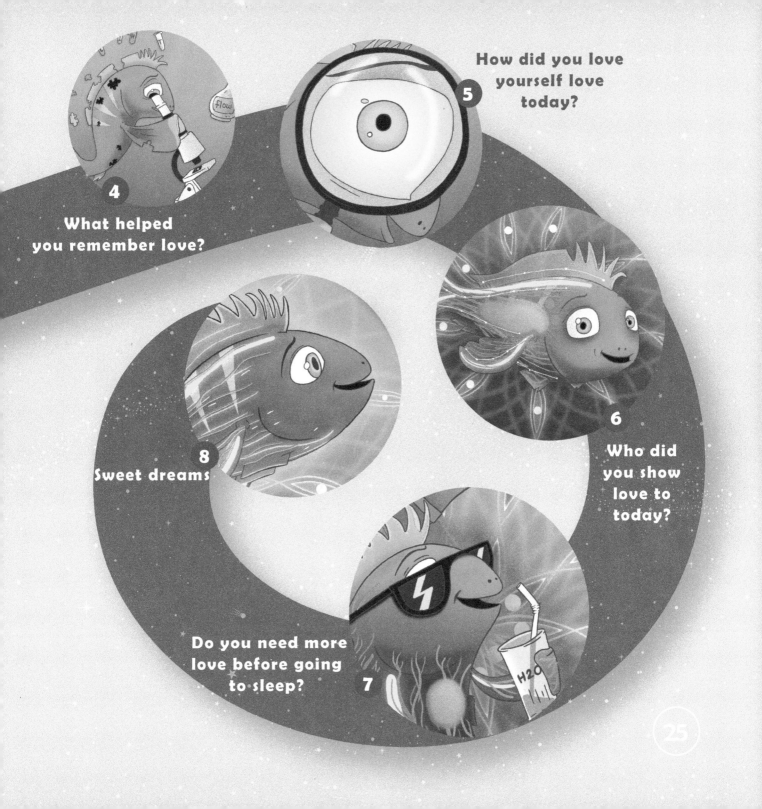

4 What helped you remember love?

5 How did you love yourself love today?

6 Who did you show love to today?

7 Do you need more love before going to sleep?

8 Sweet dreams

the collection

The Conscious Bedtime Story Club

snuggling into togetherness

the laughing witch

how diablo became Spirit

Anna Breytenbach & Andrew Newman

the tree of goodness

Andrew Newman

the elephant who tried to tiptoe

Andrew Newman

the boy who searched for silence

Andrew Newman

the dad who didn't know

Andrew Newman

we are circle people

Andrew Newman

the hug who got stuck

Andrew Newman

a little light

the fish who nearly drowned in his search for water

Andrew Newman

the prayer who searched for God

the bee who could not choose her flower

Andrew Newman

the girl with waterfall eyes

Andrew Newman

the forgetful elephant

Andrew Newman

Free downloadable coloring pages and monthly full-moon storytime
Visit www.consciousstories.com for details

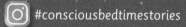 #consciousbedtimestories @Conscious Bedtime Story Club

Andrew Newman - author

Andrew Newman is the award-winning author and founder of www.ConsciousStories.com, a growing series of bedtime stories purpose-built to support parent-child connection in the last 20 minutes of the day. His professional background includes deep training in therapeutic healing work and mindfulness. He brings a calm yet playful energy to speaking events and workshops, inviting and encouraging the creativity of his audiences, children K-5, parents, and teachers alike.

Andrew has been an opening speaker for Deepak Chopra, a TEDx presenter in Findhorn, Scotland and author-in-residence at the Bixby School in Boulder, Colorado. He is a graduate of The Barbara Brennan School of Healing, a Non-Dual Kabbalistic healer and has been actively involved in men's work through the Mankind Project since 2006. He counsels parents, helping them to return to their center, so they can be more deeply present with their kids.

TED^x "Why the last 20 minutes of the day matter"

Marcelle Marais - illustrator

Marcelle Marais is an illustrator and animator born in South Africa, with 10 years experience working on a variety of projects from music videos and illustrating books to supplying the local and international advertising industry. He resides near the ocean and has a love for nature, art, literature and anything aquatic.

27

Star Counter

Every time you breathe together and read aloud, you make a star shine in the night sky.

Color in a star to count how many times you have read this book.

CPSIA information can be obtained
at www.ICGtesting.com
Printed in the USA
LVHW071921200420
654139LV00023B/391

This book belongs to:

....

....

Published by Antonina Novarese, Vertou, France
First edition
Illustrated, designed by Antonina Novarese
ISBN : 978-2-902718-00-9

Édition : Antonina Novarese, 51 rue Charles Lecour, 44120 Vertou, France
Achevé d'imprimer en mars 2020
Loi n° 49-956 du 16 juillet 1949 sur les publications destinées à la jeunesse, modifiée par la loi n°2011-525 du 17 mai 2011 : mars 2020
Dépôt légal : avril 2020

WWW.ANTONINANOVARESE.COM

NONSENSE

Edward Lear
Illustrated by
Antonina Novarese

poems for kids

There was an Old Man with a beard,
Who said, "It is just as I feared! –
    Two Owls and a Hen,
    Four Larks and a Wren,
Have all built their nests in my beard!"

There was a Young Lady of Ryde,
Whose shoe-strings were seldom untied:
    She purchased some clogs,
    And some small spotted dogs,
And frequently walked about Ryde.

There was a Young Lady whose bonnet
Came untied when the birds sat upon it;
    But she said, "I don't care!
    All the birds in the air
Are welcome to sit on my bonnet!"

There was an Old Man with a flute.
A "sarpint" ran into his boot;
    But he played day and night,
    Till the "sarpint" took flight,
And avoided that man with a flute.

There was a Young Lady whose chin
Resembled the point of a pin;
    So she had it made sharp,
    And purchased a harp,
And played several tunes with her chin.

There was an Old Man in a tree,
Who was horribly bored by a bee;
    When they said, "Does it buzz?"
    He replied, "Yes, it does!
It's a regular brute of a bee!"

There was an Old Man in a boat,
Who said, "I'm afloat! I'm afloat!"
    When they said, "No! you ain't!"
    He was ready to faint,
That unhappy Old Man in a boat.

There was a Young Lady of Portugal,
Whose ideas were excessively nautical;
    She climbed up a tree
    To examine the sea,
But declared she would never leave Portugal.

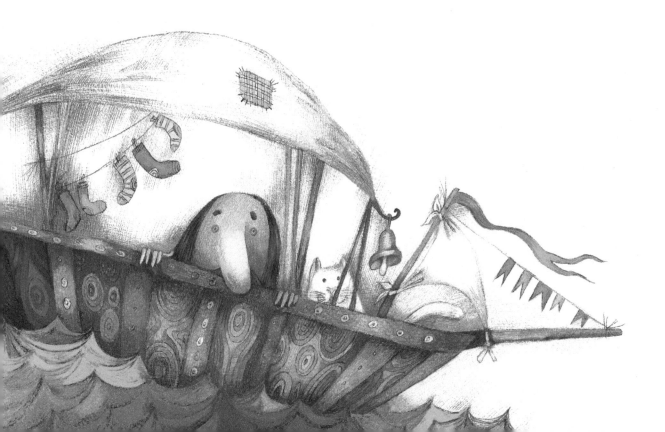

There was an Old Person of Leeds,
Whose head was infested with beads;
    She sat on a stool
    And ate gooseberry fool,
Which agreed with that Person of Leeds.

There was a Young Person of Crete,
Whose toilette was far from complete;
    She dressed in a sack
    Spickle-speckled with black,
That ombliferous Person of Crete.

There was an Old Man who supposed
That the street door was partially closed;
    But some very large rats
    Ate his coats and his hats,
While that futile old gentleman dozed.

There was an Old Person whose habits
Induced him to feed upon rabbits;
    When he'd eaten eighteen
    He turned perfectly green,
Upon which he relinquished those habits.

There was an Old Person of Dover,
Who rushed through a field of blue Clover;
    But some very large bees
    Stung his nose and his knees,
So he very soon went back to Dover.

The was a Young Lady of Bute,
Who played on a silver-gilt flute;
    She played several jigs
    To her uncle's white pigs,
That amusing Young Lady of Bute.

There was a Young Lady whose nose,
Was so long that it reached to her toes;
    So she hired an Old Lady,
    Whose conduct was steady,
To carry that wonderful nose.

There was an Old Person of Mold,
Who shrank from sensations of cold;
    So he purchased some muffs,
    Some furs and some fluffs,
And wrapped himself up from the cold.

There was an Old Man of th' Abruzzi,
So blind that he couldn't his foot see;
    When they said, "That's your toe!"
    He replied, "Is it so?"
That doubtful Old Man of th' Abruzzi.

There was an Old Man of the North,
Who fell into a basin of broth;
    But a laudable cook
    Fished him out with a hook,
Which saved that Old Man of the North.

There was an Old Man of Apulia,
Whose conduct was very peculiar;
　　He fed twenty sons
　　Upon nothing but buns,
That whimsical Man of Apulia.

There was an Old Person of Rhodes,
Who strongly objected to toads;
    He paid several cousins
    To catch them by the dozens,
That futile Old Person of Rhodes.

There was an Old Man of Cape Horn,
Who wished he had never been born;
    So he sat on a chair,
    Till he died of despair,
That dolorous Man of Cape Horn.

There was an Old Man of the South,
Who had an immoderate mouth;
    But in swallowing a dish,
    That was quite full of fish,
He was choked, that Old Man of the South.

There was an Old Man of the Dee,
Who was sadly annoyed by a flea;
    When he said, "I will scratch it,"
    They gave him a hatchet,
Which grieved that
Old Man of the Dee.

There was an Old Man of Calcutta,
Who perpetually ate bread and butter,
    Till a great bit of muffin,
    On which he was stuffing,
Choked that horrid Old Man of Calcutta.

There was an Old Man of Dundee,
Who frequented the top of a tree;
    When disturbed by the crows,
    He abruptly arose,
And exclaimed, "I'll return to Dundee."

There was an Old Person of Tring,
Who embellished his nose with a ring;
    Ha gazed at the moon
    Every evening in June,
That ecstatic Old Person in Tring.

There was an Old Man of Leghorn,
The smallest that ever was born;
     But quickly snapped up he
     Was once by a puppy,
Who devoured that Old Man of Leghorn.

There was an Old Man of the Hague,
Whose ideas were excessively vague;
     He built a balloon
     To examine the moon,
That deluded Old Man of the Hague.

There was a Young Lady of Hull,
Who was chased by a virulent bull;
    But she seized on a spade,
    And called out, "Who's afraid?"
Which distracted that virulent bull.

There was an Old Man of Whitehaven,
Who danced a quadrille with a raven;
    But they said, "It's absurd
    To encourage this bird!"
So they smashed that Old Man of Whitehaven.

There was an Old Man on whose nose,
Most birds of the air could repose;
    But they all flew away
    At the closing of day,
Which relieved that Old Man and his nose.

There was a Young Lady of Clare,
Who was sadly pursued by a bear;
 When she found she was tired,
 She abruptly expired,
That unfortunate Lady of Clare.

There was an Old Man of Aosta,
Who possessed a large cow, but he lost her;
 But they said, "Don't you see
 She has rushed up a tree?
You invidious Old Man of Aosta!"

There was an old man of Three Bridges,
Whose mind was distracted by midges,
    He sate on a wheel,
    Eating underdone veal,
Which relieved that old man of Three Bridges.

There was an old man in a Marsh,
Whose manners were futile and harsh;
    He sate on a log,
    And sang songs to a frog,
That instructive old man in a Marsh.

There was a young person in red,
Who carefully covered her head,
    With a bonnet of leather,
    And three lines of feather,
Besides some long ribands of red.

There was an old man of Blackheath,
Whose head was adorned with a wreath,
    Of lobsters and spice,
    Pickled onions and mice,
That uncommon old man of Blackheath.

There was an old man of Boulak,
Who sate on a Crocodile's back;
    But they said, "Tow'rds the night,
    He may probably bite,
Which might vex you, old man of Boulak!"

There was an old person in black,
A Grasshopper jumped on his back;
    When it chirped in his ear,
    He was smitten with fear,
That helpless old person in black.

ALSO BY ANTONINA NOVARESE:

Sister Goat

SMALL WHITE BOOK SERIES:
Frog Meets Small White
Small White
Small White and her Friends
Small White and the Wing Tailor
Small White Colouring Book

Subscribe for new release notifications at
WWW.ANTONINANOVARESE.COM

CPSIA information can be obtained
at www.ICGtesting.com
Printed in the USA
LVHW071921200420
654139LV00023B/392